PLEASE SHARE THAT PEANUT!

Please Share That Peanut!

A Preposterous Pageant
in Fourteen Acts
Concerned with the
Exquisite Joys and
Extraordinary Adventures
of
Young Ladies and Gentlemen
Engaged in
the Pleasurable Practice
of
SHARING

by Sesyle Joslin
Illustrated by Simms Taback

HARCOURT, BRACE & WORLD, INC.
NEW YORK

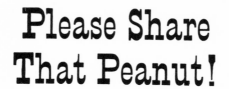

For
Alfred, Victoria, Alexandra, and Julia

PLEASE SHARE THAT PEANUT!

ACT ONE

It is dawn on the Egyptian desert, and across the sands stagger a Lady of fine quality and a Gentleman with opera glasses. They are quite lost. Silently and cautiously, they tiptoe among the mysterious pyramids and the huge dinosaurs until all at once the Lady shrieks; for there, looming ahead of them, is an enormous, pale, and bulging shape....

Scene 1

"*My* dinosaur egg," says the Lady.

"No, *mine*," says the Gentleman.

"OURS!"

ACT TWO

In India the moon gilds a magnificent palace wherein is contained much merriment. The Maharaja is giving a fancy dress ball, and there are many quite royal guests carrying on in a gay and worldly manner. Suddenly the Maharaja strikes a great gong, and everyone stands at attention as into the hushed ballroom sweeps the glamorous and fashionable Maharani....

Scene 1

"*My* rope of pearls," says the Maharani.

"No, *mine*," says the Maharaja.

"OURS!"

ACT THREE

On the stark tundra the north wind is hissing and howling, and the snow whirls about madly. Into this hazardous territory come the Admiral with a large and costly compass and the Commander wearing a scarf of a gay and warm nature. As they go hopping from glacier to glacier in rather an agile fashion, the Admiral and the Commander hear a strange kind of roar, and freezing in their tracks, they see a great furry creature lumbering toward them....

"*My* polar bear," says the Admiral.

"No, *mine*," says the Commander.

"OURS!"

ACT FOUR

At a fine old hacienda in Argentina, a sumptuous dinner party is about to begin. As gay lights and exotic music fill the air, a pony cart comes up the drive at a madcap pace and out jumps the Señorita who is a ravishing beauty, although somewhat dusty. She taps daintily upon the door and is recognized almost at once by her host. He is a dignified Caballero and very proud of his mustache, which has been in the family for years.

Suddenly the dinner bells chime, and the Caballero and the Señorita advance in debonair style to the candlelit table, where they are no sooner seated than in dashes the butler with an enormous platter....

Scene 1

"*My* peanut," says the Caballero.

"No, *mine*," says the Señorita.

"OURS!"

ACT FIVE

In the olden land of the Danes, there is a gloomy marsh
and, in it, a lady Troll with evil-gleaming eyes and a gen-
erally suspicious appearance. As the sky darkens, out of
the swamp she comes, tripping over all the serpents in
quite an awkward way. Pausing at a close-by cave, the Troll
whistles through her teeth and is joined at once by a small-
ish sort of Giant. Linking arms, they stomp over to the
home of a nearby King and rudely slay the thanes who
guard it.

Then with chuckles and cackles of a sinister quality, the
pilfering, plundering pair break into the glorious mead-
hall....

"*My* golden goblet," says the Troll.

"No, *mine*," says the Giant.

Scene 3

"OURS!"

ACT SIX

At high noon a Masked Stranger gallops into a small western town and, shooting his pistols off in a loud and rather careless manner, steals into the home of the Schoolmistress. She is famous for her charming complexion and her father's gold mine, and without further ado, the Masked Stranger energetically tosses her over his shoulder and, leaping upon his horse, kidnaps her.

The plucky Schoolmistress, however, screams and strikes out with such vigor that they both tumble, fighting, to the ground. Desperately, as the dust settles, each reaches for the heavy iron object that now lies between them....

"*My* horseshoe," says the Schoolmistress.

"No, *mine*," says the Masked Stranger.

"No, *MINE!*"

ACT SEVEN

It is midnight, and the Scullery Maid, who has flowing yellow hair and a tender heart, sets out to rescue a friend who happens to be in jail. Down into the Emperor's dungeon she boldly flits and, with a bit of hairpin, cleverly unlocks the cell containing the handsome but rather aimless Archer.

Along the castle corridors the Scullery Maid and the Archer flee, hotly pursued by a battalion of nimble-footed guards. Exhausted and despairing, they are on the very verge of being captured when suddenly they bolt into the Emperor's linen closet....

"*My* satin sheet," says the Archer.

"No, *mine*," says the Scullery Maid.

Scene 3

"OURS!"

ACT EIGHT

It is a wintry evening in Londontown, and the poor Match Girl and her sister, the poor Flower Girl, huddle close together upon the curb. Cold and hungry, the little waifs sadly watch as quite a few dashing members of Society who are wearing their best clothes pile into an elegant restaurant for some food and gaiety.

All at once a hansom cab draws up, and through their frozen tears, the sisters behold a large and sparkling fairy godmother who, hanging graciously out of the window, hands them a delightfully wrapped package.

"*My* lace gown," says the Match Girl.

Scene 2

"No, *mine*," says the Flower Girl.

Scene 3

"OURS!"

ACT NINE

A secluded tower stands silhouetted against the pale moon, and as some nearby owls hoot, a dozen portly persons dash into the building and up the winding stairs to the secret quarters of the celebrated Magician.

They are admitted at once by a more or less invisible doorkeeper, and as they sit down, quite pink with excitement, a mysterious gong bongs, and the Magician and his Assistant make their appearance....

Scene 1

"Our top hat," say the Magican and the Assistant.

"NO, *MINE!*"

ACT TEN

As the King and Queen hop into their coach, the palace serv-
ants bow, the court favorites throw kisses, and from a tur-
ret high above the moat, the little Prince and the little Princess bravely wave to their royal and departing parents. Then,
hand in hand, they descend to the cherry orchard below.
Here they innocently wander about picking buttercups and
dandelions until out of the quickening dusk there abruptly
appears a towering monster who, belching fire and flame,
leaps upon them. . . .

Scene 1

"My dragon," says the Princess.

"No, *mine*," says the Prince.

"OURS!"

ACT ELEVEN

It is a soft spring day, and down the boulevard strolls a short person in a top hat who is inclined to be a Millionaire and rather stout around the middle. He has a kindly nature and always behaves with great decency to all the pigeons, and yet he is uncommonly sad due to his loneliness. Suddenly, through his cigar smoke, the Millionaire perceives a dainty figure carrying a heavy ermine purse. It is the gentle Heiress who, taking great care not to step on any cracks, comes up the boulevard.

Quite accidentally, she bumps into the Millionaire in front of the Ice Cream Parlor, and shyly smiling, they regard one another with surprise and delight. . . .

"*My* money," says the Millionaire.

Scene 1

"*And* my money," says the Heiress.

"OURS!"

ACT TWELVE

It is a midwinter's day, and deep in the forest sit the youthful Duke and his sister, the Countess. They have been abandoned by a sinister sort of uncle, and they huddle together, covered with leaves.

All at once they become aware of a large number of wild beasts stealthily approaching, and clutching their royal robes around them, they dash off through the forest. The animals pursue them determinedly, but just as they are about to be snatched up, the desperate Duke and Countess gain sudden safety in some nearby greenery....

"*My* tree," says the Countess.

"No, *mine*," says the Duke.

"OURS!"

ACT THIRTEEN

The Imperial Ballet is about to perform at the winter palace in St. Petersburg, and the establishment is rather delirious with delight. The Czarina and her many noble houseguests glide about nibbling caviar on toast as they await the performance with merry impatience.

At last the overture is heard, the lights dim, and slowly the magnificent red and gold curtain rises. . . .

Scene 1

"*My* turn," says the Ballerina.

"No, *mine*," says the Danseur.

"OURS!"

ACT FOURTEEN

The Captain, well under his gold-braided cap, steers his yacht through the South Seas while his passenger, who is a famous Beauty, skips around the deck. It is altogether a carefree sort of cruise marred only by a terrible typhoon, which twirls up and sinks the boat.

The Captain and the Beauty swim for some hours until finally they arrive at a pleasant little tropical island. But no sooner have they crawled safely onto shore, quite wet and weary, than they are at once confronted by a great hulking shape that lies half buried in the sand....

Scene 1

"My treasure," says the Beauty.

Scene 2

"No, *mine*," says the Captain.

"OURS!"